C000268710

HOW
Yorkshire
ARE YOU?

THE YORKSHIRE CITIZENSHIP TEST

By Adrian Braddy

OVER 600 QUESTIONS TO
TEST ANY TRUE TYKE

Dalesman

Published in Great Britain in 2017 by Dalesman
an imprint of
Country Publications Ltd
The Water Mill, Broughton Hall, Skipton BD23 3AG
www.dalesman.co.uk

ISBN: 978-1-85568-363-1

Printed in China by 1010 Printing International Ltd

Contents

The Questions

Just for Fun

The Answers.....................87

Introduction

Never ask an Englishman where he is from. If he's from Yorkshire he will tell you. If he isn't, it's unfair to embarrass him.

"Being Yorkshire" is as fashionable as it's ever been. The press is awash with articles on the merits of God's Own County (or Country if tha's proper Yorksher).

Recent success in the Olympics, when Yorkshire finished twelfth in the medals table, made the rest of the world sit up and take notice.

And when newsreader Tom Bradby signed off News at Ten one August 1 with the line "Happy Yorkshire Day" it demonstrated that the state of Yorkshireness has well and truly entered the national consciousness.

Suddenly global film star Russell Crowe was promoting the joys of supping Yorkshire Tea, the Prime Minister was putting forward his candidate for "greatest living Yorkshireman" and Yorkshire was named Europe's best destination at the World Travel Awards.

Then, in the wake of a vote on Scottish devolution and the Brexit referendum, talk began of Yorkshire independence.

Serious pundits argued the case. Sir Simon Jenkins opined "Mighty Yorkshire is another country in waiting". Hear, hear!

But if Yorkshire was to become a country in its own right, would you pass the Citizenship Test? Just how Yorkshire are you?

Well, now you can find out. Complete the questions in this book and you'll be able to claim your true Yorkshire status – and bragging rights over your pals.

To help rate your Yorkshireness we've put together some fiendish challenges. Can you correctly make a Yorkshire pudding? Do you know the words to "On Ilkla Moor Baht 'at"? Can you make a good cup of tea? All these skills are assessed.

Yorkshire, for the purposes of this test, is the historic county – all three ancient Ridings plus York. It's an area with more acres than there are words in the Bible so we don't expect you to know all the answers. But we hope that by the end you'll know more about the White Rose County than you did before. The higher your score, the more Yorkshire you are.

At the back of the book there's a certificate which you can fill out on completion of the test, so you can demonstrate you have passed the Yorkshire Citizenship Test and are officially a True Tyke.

Good luck!

Adrian Braddy

The Questions

Round 1

Culture & dialect

1   When is Yorkshire Day?

2   What is a 'cratch'?

3   What equipment is needed to play the traditional Yorkshire game of Knurr and Spell?

4   Which festival traditionally takes place in Sowerby Bridge on the first weekend of September?

5   What is a Loiner?

6   What are the 'muggies' in Withernsea?

7   What are Yorkshire pennies?

8   What colour are the telephone boxes in Kingston upon Hull?

9   According to local legend, the witch Old Nan lived at which landmark in the 1700s?

10 Whitby is famous for its jet, but what is jet formed from?

Round 2

Entertainment

11 Where was Sir Patrick Stewart born?

12 Which waterfall was used as a location in the film *Robin Hood: Prince of Thieves*?

13 Where was singer Ed Sheeran born?

14 Actor Anthony Daniels – C–3PO in Star Wars – was educated at which Yorkshire school?

15 Which secondary school did Dame Judi Dench attend?

16 Where was Brian Blessed born?

17 From where was *The Good Old Days* broadcast?

18 Which railway station became "Hogsmeade" in the *Harry Potter* films?

19 In which city was comedian Frankie Howerd born?

20 Which river is the Steel River in Chris Rea's song?

Food & drink

21   Where was the first Harry Ramsden's fish and chip shop?

22   Which three towns make up the Rhubarb Triangle? (3pts)

23   In which town is the company that makes Yorkshire Tea
      based?

24   Name the fruity condiment made in Sheffield.

25   Where are Yorkshire Crisps made?

26   Which Yorkshire brewer makes Golden Pippin ale?

27   What was the nationality of the first makers of
      Wensleydale cheese?

28   What grain is parkin made from?

29   What is the slogan of Yorkshire Tea?

30   What was the York-made KitKat chocolate bar originally
      called?

Placename pictograms

Two points each. Just say what you see!

31	32

31	32

33	34
	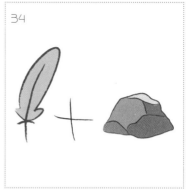
33	34

Round 5

Your score:

/10

In what year...

35 ...was the Terry's chocolate factory in York closed?

36 ...was the Humber Bridge opened to traffic?

37 ...was the final *All Creatures Great and Small* broadcast?

38 ...did Rowntree's of York patent the process of manufacturing bubbled chocolate used in its Aero bars?

39 ...did strikes halt Christmas television in the YTV region?

40 ...did Yorkshire Television begin broadcasting?

41 ...was the Great Sheffield Flood?

42 ...was the historic county of Yorkshire spilt into administrative regions?

43 ...did Leeds United win the FA Cup?

44 ...did the Bradford & Bingley brand disappear from the nation's high streets?

Yorkshire photofit

Which famous Yorkshiremen and women make up these hybrids?

45

45 a)

b)

c)

d)

e)

47 a)

b)

c)

d)

e)

f)

46

46 a)

b)

c)

d)

47

Famous firsts

48   What did York-born Joseph Aloysius Hansom invent?

49   What was founded by Settle-born Benjamin Waugh?

50   What invention of Pontefract-born John Harrison transformed long-distance sea travel?

51   What did Leeds bricklayer Joseph Aspdin invent?

52   Who founded the seaside resort of Saltburn-by-the-Sea?

53   Which two famous chocolate bars were invented by Rowntree in 1935? (2pts)

54   What is Henry Henderson best known for?

55   What did Percy Shaw, of Boothtown, Halifax, invent?

56   What familiar road markings were created by Elslack-born George Charlesworth?

57   How did Rev Sylvia Mutch make history in York in 1987?

58 Who wrote the sonnets "Malham Cove" and "Gordale"?

59 Who wrote *Billy Liar*?

60 In which city was Alan Bennett born?

61 Who wrote the poem "The Licorice Fields at Pontefract"?

62 "In all England, I do not believe that I could have fixed on a situation so completely removed from the stir of society." This line comes from the first chapter of which Yorkshire novel?

63 In which city was the poet WH Auden born?

64 Who wrote the children's book *The Christmas Day Kitten*?

65 What age was Charlotte Brontë when she died in 1855?

66 Name Bingley–born John Braine's first novel.

67 What does the J B in J B Priestley stand for?

Round 9

Past times

68   What damaged the spire of Filey Methodist Church in 1931?

69   What was the original name of the *Yorkshire Post*?

70   For what reason was William Byg of Wombwell charged with heresy in 1465?

71   Which town was called Treske in the *Domesday Book*?

72   What were Tom Puddings?

73   What was the Scarborough hotel destroyed by a landslip in 1993?

74   What was the name of Yorkshire's last deep coal mine?

75   What is the modern name for Eboracum?

76   What was the original name of the Yorkshire Bank?

77   Which castle was damaged by shells on 16 December 1914?

Round 10

People

78 Saltaire was founded by which philanthropist?

79 Where was Captain James Cook born?

80 Who was The Mouseman?

81 What is the name of William Hague's wife?

82 Which former MP was the first presenter of *Calendar* on Yorkshire TV?

83 In which village was Michael Parkinson born?

84 Who is television's The Yorkshire Vet?

85 Who officially opened Eureka!, the national children's museum in Halifax, in 1992?

86 By what name is Ursula Southeil better known?

87 Which two prime ministers spent part of their childhoods in Huddersfield? (2pts)

Round
11

Places

Your
score:

/12

88 Which town is believed to have been the location of England's last witch–burning?

89 Where in Yorkshire was actor Clark Gable stationed during the Second World War?

90 Where would you find the Piece Hall?

91 Britain's oldest registered visitor attraction is in Yorkshire. What is it?

92 Where is the World Coal Carrying Championship held?

93 Where would you find Europe's only grey reef sharks?

94 Name the Yorkshire Three Peaks. (3pts)

95 Whitby lies at the mouth of which river?

96 Where are the Devil's Arrows to be found?

97 On which river does Wetherby stand?

Round 12

Placename pictograms

Two points each. Just say what you see!

98

98

99

99

100

100

101

Zzzzz...

101

Pot luck

102   How many steps lead up to Whitby Abbey?

103   What was the A1 previously known as?

104   When is market day in Leyburn?

105   What is the name of the ropemakers at Hawes?

106   The name of Yorkshire-based supermarket ASDA is an
       abbreviation of what?

107   To which saint is York Minster dedicated?

108   Who, or what, are the King and Queen of Holderness?

109   How many stained-glass windows are there in York
       Minster?

110   What is merrils?

111   Which national retail chain, famous for its low prices, has its
       base in Normanton?

Round 14

Entertainment

112   Where were the Chuckle Brothers born?

113   Whose catchprase is "Through t' keyhole"?

114   Where was singer Joe Cocker born?

115   Which York–born actress was made a Dame in 1988?

116   Which bridge featured in both *Billy Elliot* and *Auf Wiedersehen, Pet*?

117   Who was the longest–serving *Emmerdale* character?

118   Which North Riding–born entertainer's catchphrase was, "You'll like this, not a lot, but you'll like it"?

119   Which Spice Girl was born in Leeds?

120   Where was the film *Rita, Sue and Bob Too!* set?

121   Which TV series was filmed around Marsden, Slaithwaite, Baildon and Meltham?

Round
15

Places

122 Which West Yorkshire hamlet declared independence in 1989?

123 Is Robin Hood's Bay north or south of Whitby?

124 Where would you find a theatre inside a cattle mart?

125 Where were Jowett cars built?

126 Which river flows through Littondale?

127 Where was the silk for the late Queen Mother's wedding dress produced?

128 In which dale is Pateley Bridge?

129 In 2007, BBC Breakfast viewers voted which town's high street the best in Britain?

130 Stamford Bridge stands on which river?

131 Where is the oldest chemist shop in England?

Round 16

Bio-pics

Three points each. Guess these famous Yorkshire names from the photo clues.

132

132

133

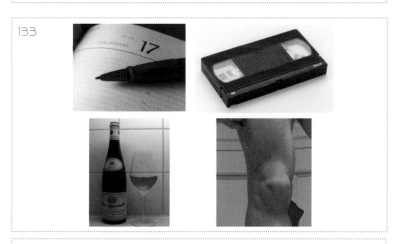

133

Round 17

People

134   For what are Elsie Wright and Frances Griffiths famous?

135   What is the name of The Yorkshire Shepherdess?

136   Which actor has, for several decades, played the dame at York Theatre Royal's annual pantomime?

137   Where was sculptor Henry Moore born?

138   Which British Prime Minister was born in Morley?

139   Which famous thief was hanged in York in 1739?

140   What was the name of the Menston-born creator of Lassie, the fictional collie?

141   Where was actress Dame Diana Rigg born?

142   Joseph Priestly, discoverer of oxygen, was born where?

143   Which captain was the game Captain's Mistress, a forerunner to Connect 4, supposedly named after?

Record breakers

144   What is Yorkshire's longest river?

145   Where would you find the world's oldest sweet shop?

146   How long is the Pennine Way?

147   What is England's highest inn?

148   What is the name of the world's oldest surviving lifeboat, which is housed at Redcar?

149   Which Yorkshire river is said to be the shortest in England?

150   Which town is home to the oldest state school in England?

151   Name the longest single-span suspension bridge in the UK.

152   What is the name of the highest, longest and deepest canal tunnel in the country?

153   In which year was Yorkshire's worst winter in living memory?

Round
19

Sr Sport

154 With which sport would you associate Sheffield's Crucible Theatre?

155 Which team is the only professional football club in England to wear claret and amber?

156 Which Yorkshire cricketer captained England to an Ashes victory in 2005?

157 What was the home town of England footballer Michael Dawson?

158 Which race, held on Boxing Day, has been dominated by the Brownlee brothers in recent years?

159 Name the oldest annual horse race in the English sporting calendar.

160 Which jewellers designed and manufactured the FA Cup in 1911?

161 In which sport did Andrew Triggs–Hodge win his three Olympic gold medals?

162 Who is the only player to have scored for both Sheffield football league teams in the Steel City derby?

163 In which year was the Bradford City stadium fire?

164 Which team won the FA Cup in 1911?

165 What sport is played by the Sheffield Steelers?

166 Where did the first known horse race to feature a female jockey competing against a male jockey take place?

167 Colin Montgomerie learnt his golf at which club?

168 Which club did Brian Clough manage in 1974?

169 What was the original name of Barnsley FC?

170 Where is the White Rose Polo Club based?

171 Where was Darren Gough born?

172 What is the nickname of Barnsley Football Club?

173 Where did the Yorkshire Grand Départ of 2014 finish?

Round **20**

Culture & dialect

174   The mining of which metal was once a key part of the Yorkshire Dales economy?

175   When are carlin peas traditionally eaten?

176   The first reference to which word – long associated with Scotland – actually appeared in Yorkshire in 1443?

177   What is a Ribston Pippin?

178   When are Yorkshire curd tarts traditionally eaten?

179   What does the Yorkshire dialect term "gurt" mean?

180   The words of what folk song are usually sung to the hymn tune "Cranbrook"?

181   What is the meaning of the dialect word "baht"?

182   What does the verb "laik" mean?

183   Define the dialect word "bray".

Round 21

Pot luck

Your score: /10

184 Name the Yorkshire racecourse with a straight mile.

185 What is sometimes referred to as the Tower of Spite?

186 Which Scarborough man is often referred to as the "father of aviation"?

187 What was the name given to the sapphire pendant found by metal detectorists in Wensleydale?

188 By which river is Fountains Abbey built?

189 Storm Desmond revived which waterfall in 2015?

190 What was Britain's first seaside resort?

191 What is the name of the cinema in Malton?

192 In Yorkshire dialect, what is a bobby-'oil?

193 What was unusual about a 2,000-year-old skeleton discovered in Ryedale Windy Pits in 2011?

Places

194   Which city was once said to have the highest ratio of trees to people of any city in Europe?

195   Which village holds an annual gooseberry show every August?

196   St Nicholas Fayre is one of the UK's most popular Christmas markets. Where is it held?

197   Which village is known for its gigantic meat and potato pies?

198   The bridge in which village became known locally as "election bridge"?

199   What is the motto of Middlesbrough?

200   Which town lies at the mouth of the Gypsey Race?

201   Appletreewick stands beside which river?

202   Which dales does Buttertubs Pass connect?

203 Where would you find the oldest surviving glassworks cone in Western Europe?

204 Where would you find the Illuminated Enchanted Forest?

205 Which West Yorkshire village has previously been known as Causeway End and Queenshead?

206 Doncaster lies on which river?

207 Where is the British Library's National Newspaper Building located?

208 Where would you find The Dancing Bear?

209 Where would you have found the distinctive Octagon Mill?

210 Where is the Montagu Hospital located?

211 The now-demolished former headquarters of Bradford & Bingley Building Society was designed as an abstract take on which local landmark?

212 Where in Yorkshire is ASDA's head office?

213 Where would you find the "Penny Hedge"?

Entertainment

Your score:

/ 10

214 What was the birthplace of entertainer Roy Castle?

215 On which estate was the TV series *Follyfoot* filmed?

216 Which 1978 film brought Richard Gere to Keighley?

217 Which native of York composed the James Bond theme?

218 *To Walk Invisible* was a television film about which family?

219 At which school was Channel 4's *Educating Yorkshire* set?

220 Presenter of *Top Gear* and *The Grand Tour* Richard Hammond attended which Yorkshire school?

221 The fictional Yorkshire town of Oldshaw was the setting for which television sitcom starring Thora Hird?

222 Billy Pearce is the regular star of which theatre's pantomime?

223 Where was the actor Sir Ben Kingsley born?

Round 23

Placename pictograms

Two points each. Just say what you see!

224 	225 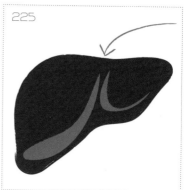
224	225

226 	227 
226	227

Literature

228 A carving in which church is said to have inspired the White Rabbit in *Alice's Adventures in Wonderland*?

229 Poet Philip Larkin was librarian at which university?

230 When Charles Dickens visited the "Yorkshire Schools" around Bowes he was researching which novel?

231 Which Yorkshire village was mentioned in the early ballad "Robin Hood and the Potter"?

232 Which Yorkshire town is mentioned in Shakespeare's *Henry IV Part 1*?

233 Who wrote, "Sheffield, I suppose, could justly claim to be called the ugliest town in the Old World"?

234 Offices in which town are said to be the inspiration behind Scrooge's counting house in Dickens' *A Christmas Carol*?

235 Brian Sinclair was known to millions by what other name?

236 Which famous author wrote *The Green Dwarf*?

237 Which Irish writer, visiting Whitby in 1890, was inspired to write his most famous work?

238 Who wrote *The Lady in the Van*?

239 Who is the earliest named English poet?

240 Which Walter Scott novel features Conisbrough Castle?

241 From where did the hero first set sail in *Robinson Crusoe*?

242 Which Dales village is said to be the setting of the novel *The Secret Garden*?

243 Which two famous writers attended the same nursery school in Upper Armley, Leeds?

244 In which village did William Wordsworth marry in 1802?

245 Which Yorkshireman served as Poet Laureate from 1984 until his death in 1988?

246 Which book features Roberta, Peter and Phyllis?

247 Which two Brontë siblings set their juvenilia in the imaginary kingdom of Gondal?

Round 26

Food & drink

Your score:

/10

248 What is the name given to the traditional Yorkshire Christmas Eve supper made from wheat porridge?

249 Which cheese was once known as Yorkshire Stilton?

250 At which Yorkshire restaurant did Marco Pierre White train?

251 Until 2012, where were After Eight mints made?

252 Where would you find Theakston's Brewery?

253 Wensleydale Cheese is a favourite food for which animated characters?

254 The recipe for what was first recorded in 1737?

255 Which town bills itself "Yorkshire's food capital"?

256 Which company has trademarked the name Fat Rascal?

257 Which town has given its name to a type of lamb chop?

Past times

258 What was the Viking name for the city of York?

259 Which newspaper first exposed the affair between Edward VIII and Mrs Simpson?

260 What was the first mainline railway to be built in Yorkshire?

261 Which town hosted Britain's first aviation meeting, in 1909?

262 Why was Timmy Feather of Stanbury well known?

263 Who or what was the Maiden of Halifax?

264 For what was Blind Jack of Knaresborough well known?

265 What met at York eleven times between 1301 and 1335?

266 The bones of what large animal were uncovered in 1851 at a brick field in Wortley, Leeds?

267 What did Vincenzo Lunardi do in 1786 in Leeds that drew thousands of spectators?

Round 28

Pot luck

Your score:

/20

268 Where was Toffee Town?

269 In dialect, what is the definition of the adjective "capped"?

270 Which prominent mast in the North York Moors shares its name with a dale?

271 What is the name of the Royal Air Force station on Snod Hill in the North York Moors?

272 Where was actor Malcolm McDowell born?

273 Where is the Copper Dragon Brewery?

274 Where would you find England's oldest forge?

275 Where can you see a pig playing bagpipes?

276 On which river is The Strid?

277 Founded in 627 AD, which Yorkshire school is said to be the fourth oldest in the world?

278 What would you now find in what was originally Hawes Railway Station?

279 At which hotel was the Northern Rugby Football Union formed?

280 What landmark was made by schoolmaster John Hodgson and his class in 1857?

281 According to local tradition, Guy Fawkes rang the bells in which village's church?

282 In 1806, George Gowthorpe of Patrington sold what for twenty guineas in Hull marketplace?

283 Charles I stayed as a guest in 1640 and was imprisoned in 1647 at the same house in which town?

284 What was formed in a meeting room above the Old Cock inn, Halifax, in the 1850s?

285 What was described as "England's only truly spectacular road" by Jeremy Clarkson?

286 Where was singer Tony Christie born?

287 Which famous brand was founded in Batley in 1853?

Places

288 On which two rivers would you find similar natural
features both known as God's Bridge? (2pts)

289 Which town is home to England's oldest state school?

290 How is the "Yorkshire Matterhorn" better known?

291 In which town would you find the Pier Towers but no pier?

292 Dobroyd Castle stands above which town?

293 Which town was reportedly founded by Thorgils Skarthi?

294 Which place was once known as the Merrie City?

295 The Devil's Arrows stand close to which river?

296 Which dale had its own light railway, which operated
between 1907 and 1929?

297 Which town was named happiest in Britain for three years
in a row?

Bio-pics

Three points each. Guess these famous Yorkshire names from the photo clues.

298

298

299

299

300 Who famously said, "I would have died for Yorkshire. I suppose once or twice I nearly did"?

301 Where in Yorkshire were John Noakes, Frank Worthington and Linda Barker all born?

302 What is the name of the *Woman's Hour* presenter who was born in Barnsley?

303 Singer Jarvis Cocker was born where?

304 Which Yorkshireman reinvented the wheel?

305 Which Skipton-born former Chancellor of the Exchequer is credited with coining the term "nanny state"?

306 Name the Yorkshire-born chemist who became the first Briton in space.

307 On which newspaper did Patrick Stewart begin his career, before becoming an actor?

308 On which York street is it said Guy Fawkes was born?

309 Who, in 2015, replaced Patrick Stewart as Chancellor of the University of Huddersfield?

310 Which *Friends* guest star was born in Pontefract?

311 Which Keighley—born singer was a coach on *The Voice UK*?

312 Who suggested Halifax as the location for the National Children's Museum?

313 In which Dales village did both writer Sir Arthur Conan Doyle and soap star Kate Ford get married?

314 Which actor died at the Midland Hotel, Bradford, after performing at the Theatre Royal in the city?

315 Which Bingley astronomer coined the term "the Big Bang"?

316 What was founded by Thirsk—born Thomas Lord?

317 Dewsbury's Betty Boothroyd served as what in the 1990s?

318 What was the real name of author James Herriot?

319 Who did David Cameron call the greatest living Yorkshireman?

Round
32

Entertainment

320 In which village was *Emmerdale Farm* originally filmed?

321 Which town was the location for *Open All Hours*?

322 DJ Chris Moyles first worked on hospital radio in which town or city?

323 Which band had a chart hit called "I Predict a Riot"?

324 The mother of which Yorkshire–born Hollywood film star ran a small hotel in Bridlington?

325 Which band had a chart hit with "The Floral Dance" in 1977?

326 Where was Brian Glover born?

327 Name the 2014 Christmas movie filmed in locations including Leeds, Wetherby and Bradford.

328 Which town became "Oxley" in TV series *The Chase*?

329 *Broadchurch* star Jodie Whittaker was born where?

Famous firsts

330 Where was Elastoplast invented?

331 With what invention is Harry Brearley of Sheffield credited?

332 Where was Bamforth & Co Ltd, the film pioneers, founded?

333 Which Yorkshireman invented soda water?

334 Which Yorkshireman invented the hydraulic press?

335 For what reason is the Leeds–built Blackburn Type D
     Monoplane unique?

336 What was invented by Rotherham's Sir Donald Bailey?

337 What world first supposedly took place in Leeds in 1888?

338 Isabel Denton is credited with inventing straw hats. Where
     did she live?

339 What is it that William Strickland, of Boynton, near
     Bridlington, is said to have introduced to England?

Pot luck

340 What was unusual about the money that paid for the construction of the Church of Christ the Consoler, Skelton–cum–Newby?

341 What is Leeds ironmonger James Henry Atkinson credited with inventing?

342 Where would you find the headquarters of the Rugby Football League?

343 Who was the first captain of Yorkshire County Cricket Club in 1863?

344 Seabrook crisps, according to the packaging, are "lovingly made in Yorkshire" – but where in Yorkshire?

345 Which Yorkshire band took their name from a South African football club?

346 Which business began life in 1899 as an egg and butter stall in Rawson Market, Bradford?

347 According to the 2017 television commercial, who is Yorkshire Tea's head of interviews?

348 At which village were the original "Darby and Joan" said to have lived?

349 What famous former resident of Knaresborough has a moth named after her?

350 The Sydney Harbour Bridge was designed and built by which North Riding firm?

351 Name the first woman and amateur footballer to reach over 100 caps for England.

352 It is the name of a pub in Hull but who holds the title Admiral of the Humber?

353 What is a ginnel?

354 Where was Tetley's Brewery founded in 1822?

355 Which famous artist was commissioned by the Huddersfield Corporation to paint the town in 1965?

356 "Remember Scarborough", a British propaganda campaign of the First World War, referred to what?

357 On which television programme was the Four Yorkshiremen sketch first performed?

Record breakers

Your score:

/10

358 What is said to be the largest maze in the UK?

359 Which cliff is the highest point on the east coast?

360 Which Yorkshire pub is said to be the oldest in Britain?

361 What is England's oldest one–day agricultural show?

362 Which village is said to have the longest hyphenated place name in England, with 29 characters?

363 In which village is England's tallest standing stone?

364 Where can you find what is claimed to be Yorkshire's narrowest street?

365 Where would you find Europe's longest roller coaster?

366 What has the longest country house façade in Europe?

367 Where would you find what is claimed to be the country's highest permanent maypole?

Placename pictograms

Two points each. Just say what you see!

368

368

369

369

370

370

371

371

Round 37

Places

372 The first recorded case of an English monarch handing Maundy money to the poor took place in which town?

373 Which town became home to the UK's first bottle bank in 1977?

374 Which town was home to the giant William Bradley?

375 According to legend, which town got its name after a king's ring was found in the stomach of a fish?

376 Which visitor attraction is billed as "the strangest place in the world"?

377 What is said to be the farthest inland working port in Britain?

378 In which town does the Cleveland Way start?

379 Which city has the dialling code 01482?

380 At which village do the Coast to Coast Walk and the Pennine Way footpaths cross?

381 Which popular tourist attraction was initially called the Yorkshire Zoological Gardens?

382 Which former borough was raised to city status in 1888?

383 Which city's name is said to originate from a word meaning "people of the fast-flowing river"?

384 Where is the annual Fishermen and Firemen's Boxing Day football match held?

385 In which town is auction house Tennants based?

386 Where is the Yorkshire Oaks flat horse race held?

387 In which Dales village can you find Little Emily's Bridge?

388 Malton and Norton lie on opposite sides of which river?

389 In which town would you find the White Horse Inn, which is still gas-lit to this day?

390 In 1665, which village did James II, then Duke of York, describe as a "paradise on Earth"?

391 Which waterway marked its bicentenary in 2015?

Literature

392 Where were James Herriot (Alf Wight)'s ashes scattered?

393 About which town did Daniel Defoe write, "We were agreeably surprised to find so handsome a town, and such good accommodations, in so mountainous a country"?

394 What was the maiden name of James's wife Helen in the James Herriot books?

395 In which year were the Brontë novels *Wuthering Heights*, *Jane Eyre* and *Agnes Grey* all published?

396 Which fictitious Yorkshire Riding did Winifred Holtby take as the title for a series of novels?

397 What novel begins with the line "There was no possibility of taking a walk that day"?

398 Which castle is famous for its cylindrical keep and for inspiring Sir Walter Scott's *Ivanhoe*?

399 Of which town or city did Charles Dickens say "the queerest place, with the strangest people in it, leading the oddest lives"?

400 What was the inspiration for Lewthwaite Crag in Charles
     Kingsley's *The Water Babies*?

401 Which Shakespeare play includes the line "Welcome, my
     lord, to this brave town of York"?

402 "It is a Yorkshire habit to say what you think with blunt
     frankness" is a quote from which famous children's book?

403 Where did Alf Wight (James Herriot) spend his
     honeymoon?

404 For what is Cleckheaton-born Roger Hargreaves best
     remembered?

405 Who wrote *Room at the Top* while he was a librarian in his
     home town of Bingley?

406 Which remote building is sometimes said to have inspired
     Wuthering Heights?

407 Where did Leo Walmsley set his Bramblewick novels?

408 The OED credits which writer with coining phrases
     including "Wild West" and "raised eyebrow"?

409 Who is the "Bard of Barnsley"?

Pot luck

410   Which team pipped Yorkshire on the final day to win the cricket County Championship in 2016?

411   In 1915, Addingham School closed early to economise on what?

412   Bradford City FC started life as a rugby league club with what name?

413   Which Yorkshire breed of horse is said to be the oldest established English breed and is used to pull carriages in royal processions to this day?

414   Thomas Crapper, of Thorne, owned the world's first showroom for what?

415   Which famous chain of shops began with a market stall in Leeds in 1884?

416   Which breed of dog was exbitited for the first time at a Yorkshire championship dog show in 1864?

417   Who tramped to London from Appletreewick as a boy and went on to become Lord Mayor of London twice?

Bio-pics

Three points each. Guess these
historical Yorkshire personalities
from the photo clues.

418

418

419

419

Round 41

Entertainment

Your score:

/ 8

420   What was the location for the 2006 ITV adaptation of *Mansfield Park*?

421   Where was the real-life location of Ashfordly Police Station in TV series *Heartbeat*?

422   What is the name of the singer from Settle who topped the singles chart in 2013?

423   What is the name of the Huddersfield-born writer of *Last Tango in Halifax*?

424   Which Yorkshire actress has been photographed naked, holding a lobster?

425   Where was *Downton Abbey* and *Cinderella* star Sophie McShera born?

426   A 2013 series on BBC 2 focused on Bradford. What was its name?

427   Which Yorkshire theatre stages more productions each year than any other outside London?

Round 42

Record breakers

428 Which is the smallest city in Yorkshire?

429 Who was named the greatest ever Yorkshireman by a BBC poll in 2004?

430 What is the oldest football club in the world?

431 Where would you find the world's only submarium?

432 Where would you find the largest megalith in the UK?

433 Which river is said to be the fastest-flowing in England?

434 Where would you find the largest area of heather moorland in England?

435 What is the oldest working cable tramway in Britain?

436 Where would you find what is claimed to be the "oldest surviving complete lighthouse in England"?

437 What is known as the smallest stately home in England?

438   Which West Riding town is home to Silentnight Beds and a
Rolls Royce factory?

439   Where is the Streetlife Museum of Transport?

440   Which river runs through Tadcaster?

441   The hamlet of Totties is near which town?

442   Cannons used on the HMS *Victory* and for the American
War of Independence were made in which town?

443   In which town would you find Barkers department store?

444   Where would you find Cosh Inside?

445   In 2002, which city was named "most haunted in Europe"?

446   In which village does the Coast to Coast walk end?

447   In which town would you find The Wensleydale School?

448 In which Dales village hall was a bugging device discovered in a wall socket in 2006?

449 In which town is the New Year tradition of scrambling still kept alive?

450 Which city is home to an ice trail?

451 In which village can you find a church that's the second of its kind to be built from ferro-concrete?

452 Which town was the first in the UK to have a formal "twin town"?

453 Which town holds an annual bed race?

454 Which town was home to a prison between 1788 and 2013?

455 Helmsley is in which dale?

456 Where was RAF Hunmanby Moor?

457 In which village can you find the country's oldest independent cooperative store?

458 Where is Old Bartle burned each year?

Pot luck

459 Name the Pontefract MP who was also a prize–fighter and horse racer.

460 Which town gave its name to a plough invented by one of its residents?

461 What is Yorkshire's oldest brewery?

462 What is a tup?

463 At what age was William Wilberforce, who led the movement to eradicate the slave trade, elected to parliament?

464 Where would you find the "Virgin Viaduct"?

465 A large collection of the work of which famous artist is on permanent display at Salts Mill, Saltaire?

466 In Yorkshire dialect, what does "sitha" mean?

467 The small brick–built and castellated structure on the banks of Bedale Beck was used for storing what?

Round
45

Bio-pics

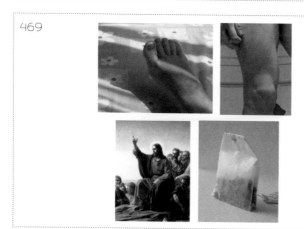

Three points each. Guess these
famous Yorkshire names from the
photo clues.

468

H +

468

469

469

Round **46**

Record breakers

470 What is the highest peak in the historic county of Yorkshire?

471 Which town is home to what is said to be Europe's smallest Ultra 4K cinema?

472 In which town or city would you find what is claimed to be England's smallest window?

473 From 1977 to 2014 a tortoise called Charlie held the world speed record he set at the National Tortoise Championships in which town?

474 What is the world's oldest continuously working public railway?

475 What is the name of the power station with the highest generating capacity in the UK?

476 Which tree, now sadly dead, holds the record of being the largest-girthed English Oak ever recorded in Britain?

477 What archery contest is claimed to be the world's longest established and oldest recorded sporting event?

Places

478 Which city was described as a "large farming village" in 1086?

479 In which town or city does a hornblower set the watch?

480 Where would you find the only mainland breeding colony of gannets in England?

481 What does the Scammonden Bridge cross?

482 Where, in 1904, were church bells rung at the bottom of a coal pit shaft?

483 Beside which road would you find Robin Hood's Well?

484 Which village was home to a man who, when jilted, spent the rest of his life in bed?

485 Where would you find the last working windmill north of the Humber?

486 The practice of changing the date of Easter each year originated in which seaside town?

Entertainment

487 Where was *Dawn of the Planet of the Apes* actor Toby
Kebbell born?

488 Scarborough-born Charles Laughton won an Oscar for
which film?

489 Dame Judi Dench made headlines for receiving which
unusual gift on her 81st birthday?

490 ITV's *Victoria* was largely filmed at The Yorkshire Studios.
Where are these studios located?

491 Which village was used as the setting for Darrowby in
television's *All Creatures Great and Small*?

492 What was the name of the bus featured on BBC Four's *All
Aboard! The Country Bus*?

493 In which village near Doncaster was *Open All Hours* writer
Roy Clarke born?

494 Which North Yorkshire actress played Victorian serial killer
Mary Ann Cotton on TV?

495 Name the town that shares its name with a film starring Judi Dench and Ian Holm?

496 What was the first programme broadcast by Yorkshire Television following the official opening ceremony?

497 Which cycling—themed film, made in Yorkshire, starred John McCallum, Honor Blackman and Diana Dors?

498 Which Hull band had a chart—topping album called *Carry On Up The Charts*?

499 Which famous processional hymn was written by a curate at Horbury, near Wakefield?

500 J Arthur Rank, founder of Pinewood Studios and the Rank Organisation, was born where?

501 What famous building appeared as Dr Forrest's surgery in the 1970 film *The Railway Children*?

502 Bradford—born Harry Corbett, creator of glove puppet character Sooty, was the nephew of which famous fellow Yorkshireman?

503 Which Glusburn—born writer wrote the screenplays for *Slumdog Millionaire* and *The Full Monty*?

Yorkshire brands

Can you identify these well-known Yorkshire companies or products from a section of their logo?

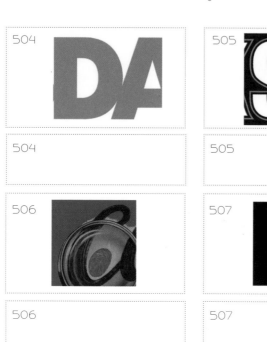

504	505
504	505
506	507
506	507
508	509
508	509

510

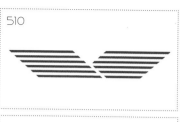

511

510

511

512

513

512

513

514

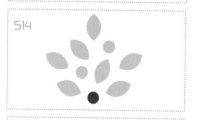

515

514

515

516

517

516

517

Pot luck

518   What is the highest operational railway station in England?

519   Which city's motto is "Progress, Industry, Humanity"?

520   From which village was *Dalesman* magazine first published in 1939?

521   Where would you find Ye Olde Naked Man?

522   Which town's mayor gives "shillings" to elderly residents every December?

523   Two of the four surviving bridge chapels in England can be found in Yorkshire. Where? (2pts)

524   Name the lake near Sutton Bank with, according to legend, a village submerged beneath it.

525   Which East Riding village claims to be the largest in England?

526   Where would you find Britain's only Swastika Stone?

527 Name Britain's oldest working theatre still in its original form.

528 In which church would you find a pew that is believed to have originally been an opera box?

529 Where would you find the longest-running West Indian carnival in Europe?

530 What was the largest and bloodiest battle ever fought on English soil?

531 Which Leeds-born author's books have sold more than 92 million copies since her debut novel was published in 1979?

532 After London, which town or city was hardest hit by the Blitz?

533 Bette Davis made a film in Malhamdale in 1951. What was it called?

534 Which place did Daniel Defoe describe as "very thin of towns and people"?

535 What was the name of Jelly Babies when they were originally produced, in Sheffield, to commemorate the end of the First World War?

536 What is the name of the bridge over the Esk built, according to legend, to stop lovers from being separated?

537 Where was the first ever formal brass band contest held?

538 What was the name of the extravagant regional dish made from a variety of game, poultry, bacon and other delights, topped off with pastry?

539 Which Yorkshirewoman would you associate with the word "ology"?

540 Translate the dialect phrase "frame thissen".

541 Which star of the "wireless" used Yorkshire catchphrases including "'Ow do?" and "Are you courtin'"?

542 Which stately home has twice played the part on screen of the fictional Brideshead?

543 In 2015, which view was voted the best in Yorkshire?

544 Arthur Wood, of Heckmondwike, wrote the theme tune for which soap opera?

545 Which Bradford-born former Yorkshire TV newsreader became a Labour MP?

Round 51

The Yorkshire Rose

What's wrong with the following roses?

546

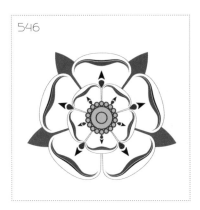

- ☐ a) It's upside down
- ☐ b) Not enough leaves
- ☐ c) Wrong colour
- ☐ d) Nothing

547

- ☐ a) It's upside down
- ☐ b) Not enough leaves
- ☐ c) Wrong colour
- ☐ d) Nothing

548

- ☐ a) It's upside down
- ☐ b) Not enough leaves
- ☐ c) Wrong colour
- ☐ d) Nothing

549

- ☐ a) It's upside down
- ☐ b) Not enough leaves
- ☐ c) Wrong colour
- ☐ d) Nothing

Yorkshire filming locations

Which films or television programmes feature scenes filmed in the following Yorkshire locations?

550 Goathland Station

☐ a) *Yanks*
☐ b) *Harry Potter*
☐ c) *The Railway Children*
☐ d) *Emmerdale Farm*

551 Hardraw Force

☐ a) *Robin Hood: Prince of Thieves*
☐ b) *Calendar Girls*
☐ c) *The Princess Bride*
☐ d) *Fairytale: A True Story*

552 Kilnsey Crag

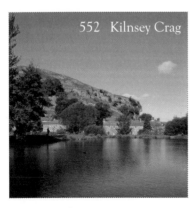

☐ a) *Last of the Summer Wine*
☐ b) *Heartbeat*
☐ c) *The Secret Garden*
☐ d) *Calendar Girls*

553 Holmfirth

☐ a) *Emmerdale Farm*
☐ b) *Women in Love*
☐ c) *Last of the Summer Wine*
☐ d) *Brassed Off*

554 Oakworth Station

555 Askrigg

- [ ] a) *Yanks*
- [ ] b) *The Railway Children*
- [ ] c) *All Creatures Great and Small*
- [ ] d) *Harry Potter*

- [ ] a) *Last of the Summer Wine*
- [ ] b) *Where the Heart Is*
- [ ] c) *The Royal*
- [ ] d) *All Creatures Great and Small*

556 Castle Howard

557 Harewood House

- [ ] a) *Brideshead Revisited*
- [ ] b) *Downton Abbey*
- [ ] c) *Doctor Who*
- [ ] d) *Upstairs, Downstairs*

- [ ] a) *Downton Abbey*
- [ ] b) *Victoria*
- [ ] c) *Brideshead Revisited*
- [ ] d) *The Woman in Black*

558 Carl Wark

559 Tees Transporter Bridge

- [ ] a) *Wuthering Heights*
- [ ] b) *Rita, Sue and Bob Too!*
- [ ] c) *The Princess Bride*
- [ ] d) *To Walk Invisible*

- [ ] a) *Billy Elliot*
- [ ] b) *The Full Monty*
- [ ] c) *Brassed Off*
- [ ] d) *Four Lions*

Round
53

What city?

Your score:

/12

The photos below show scenes in Yorkshire cities from the early to mid 20th century. Can you identify each city? Two points each.

560

561

562

563

564

565

Name the view

The views shown below all appeared in a poll conducted by
Dalesman magazine in 2015 to find Yorkshire's best view. Can
you identify them?

566

566 ....

567

567 ....

568

568 ....

569

569 ....

570

570 ....

Landmark silhouettes

Can you identify these Yorkshire landmarks from their shapes?

571

571

572

572

573

573

574

574

575

575

576

576

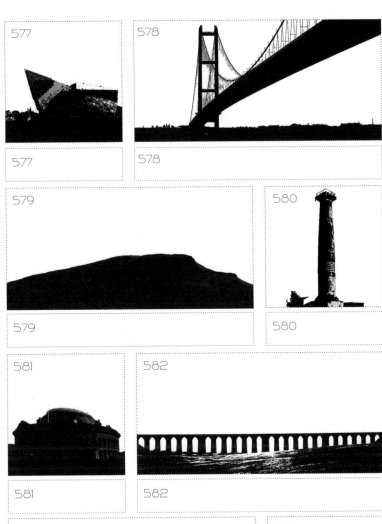

577

577

578

578

579

579

580

580

581

581

582

582

583

583

584

584

585

585

586

586

587

587

588

588

589

589

590

590

591

591

592

592

Just for Fun

The *Tea* Test

Whatever the crisis, there's nowt like a mug o' tea to put things right

Every true Yorkshireman or woman will down several pints of the life-affirming beverage each week. But what's the right way to make a cup of tea, according to the masters of the art at Taylor's of Harrogate, makers of Yorkshire Tea?

1. Which of the following should you not do?
- ☐ a) Only use expensive bottled water
- ☐ b) Only boil the water once
- ☐ c) Let the tap run for a while before boiling the kettle

2. Tea should be served in a...
- ☐ a) Polystyrene cup
- ☐ b) Mug
- ☐ c) China cup and saucer

3. How long should you let tea brew?
- ☐ a) 1–2 minutes
- ☐ b) 2–3 minutes
- ☐ c) 4–5 minutes

4. Should you squeeze the teabag before removing?
- ☐ a) Never
- ☐ b) Once, against the side
- ☐ c) Really mash it several times

5. When brewing tea in a mug, when should you add the milk?
- ☐ a) Before adding the teabag
- ☐ b) Immediately after adding the teabag
- ☐ c) After the tea has brewed

The TIGHT Test

Yorkshiremen and women are some of the most generous in the world, but they are also famously careful with their money. Take our test to find out how tight you are.

1. Have you ever tried to haggle in a charity shop?
☐ a) Yes
☐ b) No

2. Have you ever taken home shampoo sachets from hotel rooms?
☐ a) Yes
☐ b) No

3. Have you ever sneaked your own snacks into the cinema?
☐ a) Yes
☐ b) No

4. Have you ever watered down the milk?
☐ a) Yes
☐ b) No

5. Have you ever turned underwear inside out?
☐ a) Yes
☐ b) No

6. Have you ever reused a dried-out teabag?
☐ a) Yes
☐ b) No

7. Have you ever nipped to the toilet when it's your round?
☐ a) Yes
☐ b) No

8. Have you recently opened your wallet and discovered you've still got a white fiver in there?
☐ a) Yes
☐ b) No

9. Have you ever bought own-brand goods then transferred them to more expensive branded boxes?
☐ a) Yes
☐ b) No

10. Do you ever use just a single sheet of loo paper?
☐ a) Yes
☐ b) No

11. Have you ever watered down beer when you have guests?
☐ a) Yes
☐ b) No

12. Have you ever served visiting guests wine in extra-small glasses?
☐ a) Yes
☐ b) No

13. Have you ever used, or would you ever consider using, a two-for-one voucher on a first date?
☐ a) Yes
☐ b) No

14. Have you ever ironed out Christmas wrapping paper to use for someone else?
☐ a) Yes
☐ b) No

15. Have you ever cut up a toothpaste tube to get the last bits out?
☐ a) Yes
☐ b) No

16. Have you ever stalked the shop assistant with the price-reducing sticker machine around the supermarket?
☐ a) Yes
☐ b) No

17. Have you ever found moths flying from your wallet?
☐ a) Yes
☐ b) No

18. Have you ever taken lightbulbs with you when you moved house?
☐ a) Yes
☐ b) No

19. Have you ever made a bar of soap from the remnants of several old slivers?
☐ a) Yes
☐ b) No

20. Have you ever asked for a doggy bag after dinner at a friend's house?
☐ a) Yes
☐ b) No

21. Have you ever, after you've finished making the tea, left the oven door open to heat the kitchen?
☐ a) Yes
☐ b) No

22. And lastly, how many times a day do you utter the phrase "'Ow much?!"
☐ a) Never
☐ b) One to three
☐ c) Four or more

The *Yorkshire* Test *Pudding*

For centuries there have been debates about the best way to serve up Yorkshire puddings. Being able to cook a good Yorkshire pud is a true test of Yorkshireness.

When her Yorkshire puddings failed to rise, *Great British Bake Off* contestant Val Stones, from Doncaster, said, "They're not going to let me into Yorkshire. Ever again." It really is that important.

In 2008 the Royal Society of Chemistry set out to create the "definitive recipe".

Chemical scientist, author and Yorkshireman John Emsley claimed that people not from that county rarely produced worthy Yorkshire puddings. "It's in the blood and instinct of people born and raised there," he said. "You can always tell from the look and taste if the cook has the right touch and it is almost pitiful to observe the stuff that comes from some southern ovens – flat, pale and soggy much of the time."

Based on the doctor's research, can you answer our Yorkshire pudding test?

1. What fat should you use?
☐ a) Beef dripping
☐ b) Vegetable oil
☐ c) Lard
☐ d) Truffle oil

2. What flour should you use?
☐ a) Wholemeal flour
☐ b) Cornflour
☐ c) Plain flour
☐ d) Self-raising flour

3. What should be the consistency of the batter?
☐ a) Thick enough to stand a spoon in
☐ b) Lumpy
☐ c) Gritty
☐ d) Smooth and thin

4. When the batter is finished, you should...

- ☐ a) Immediately pour into tins
- ☐ b) Chill it in the fridge
- ☐ c) Stand it at room temperature for 10 minutes
- ☐ d) Leave it to stand for three days

5. How hot should the fat be before you add the batter?

- ☐ a) Chilled
- ☐ b) Room temperature
- ☐ c) Quite warm
- ☐ d) So hot it sets off the smoke alarm

6. How long should you keep the batter in the oven?

- ☐ a) 5 minutes
- ☐ b) 10 to 15 minutes
- ☐ c) 25 to 30 minutes
- ☐ d) One hour

7. What is the optimum height your puddings should rise to?

- ☐ a) 1 inch
- ☐ b) 2 inches
- ☐ c) 4 inches
- ☐ d) 10 inches

8. When and how should you serve the pudding?

- ☐ a) Alongside your meat and vegetables as a main course
- ☐ b) Before the main course, doused in gravy
- ☐ c) After the main course
- ☐ d) For breakfast

The *Anthem* Test

The words of Yorkshire dialect anthem "On Ilkla Mooar Baht 'At" will be as familiar to a true Tyke as their own name. So we know you'll have absolutely no problem filling in the missing lyrics below.

1. Wheear 'as tha _____ sin' Ah saw thee, Ah saw thee?
☐ a) bin
☐ b) bahn
☐ c) baht

2. Tha's bin a cooartin' Mary _____
☐ a) Sue
☐ b) Kelly
☐ c) Jane

3. Tha's bahn to catch thy _____ o' cowd
☐ a) cough
☐ b) deeath
☐ c) worms

4. Then us'll ha' to _____ thee
☐ a) eyt
☐ b) getten
☐ c) bury

5. Then t'worms'll come an' eyt thee _____
☐ a) oop
☐ b) trousers
☐ c) ducks

6. Then t'ducks'll come an' _____ up t'worms
☐ a) baht
☐ b) getten
☐ c) eyt

7. Then us'll go an' eyt up t'_____
☐ a) ducks
☐ b) worms
☐ c) thee

8. Then us'll all ha' _____ thee
☐ a) getten
☐ b) cooarted
☐ c) etten

9. That's wheear we get us _____ back
☐ a) trousers
☐ b) ooan
☐ c) cowd

And for a bonus point, try a rousing rendition of the chorus to finish:
On Ilkla Mooar baht 'at
On Ilkla Mooar baht 'at
On Ilkla Mooar baht 'at!

The FOOTBALL Test

In 1857, six years before the Football Association rules were created, officials at the world's first football club, Sheffield FC, penned the Sheffield Rules.

These pioneering laws of football first introduced the concepts of corners, throw-ins and free kicks for fouls, placing the origins of the world's most popular sport firmly in Yorkshire.

Of course, any true Tyke should know their football rules inside out, so which of the following are genuine laws from the 1858 version of the Sheffield Rules and which are from the official rules of modern-day hockey?

1. The kick-off from the middle must be a place kick.
☐ a) Football
☐ b) Hockey

2. Captains must wear a distinctive arm-band or similar distinguishing article on an upper arm or shoulder or over the upper part of a sock.
☐ a) Football
☐ b) Hockey

3. It is not lawful to take the ball off the ground (except in touch) for any purpose whatever.
☐ a) Football
☐ b) Hockey

4. A fair catch is a catch from any player provided the ball has not touched the ground or has not been thrown from touch and is entitled to a free kick.
☐ a) Football
☐ b) Hockey

5. Kick out must not be more than 25 yards out of goal.
☐ a) Football
☐ b) Hockey

6. Charging is fair in case of a place kick.
☐ a) Football
☐ b) Hockey

7. A match consists of two periods of 35 minutes and a half-time interval of 5 minutes.
☐ a) Football
☐ b) Hockey

8. Players must not intimidate or impede another player.
☐ a) Football
☐ b) Hockey

9. Pushing with the hands is allowed but no hacking or tripping up is fair under any circumstances whatever.
☐ a) Football
☐ b) Hockey

10. A goal must be kicked but not from touch nor by a free kick from a catch.
☐ a) Football
☐ b) Hockey

11. Players are permitted to wear gloves for protection which do not increase the natural size of the hands signicantly.
☐ a) Football
☐ b) Hockey

12. The whistle must be blown decisively and loudly enough for all involved in the match to be able to hear it. This does not mean long, loud whistling at all times.
☐ a) Football
☐ b) Hockey

13. The goal-posts must not extend vertically beyond the cross-bar and the cross-bar must not extend horizontally beyond the goal-posts.
☐ a) Football
☐ b) Hockey

14. Each player must provide himself with a red and dark blue flannel cap, one colour to be worn by each side.
☐ a) Football
☐ b) Hockey

15. A ball in touch is dead, consequently the side that touches it down must bring it to the edge of the touch and throw it straight out from touch.
☐ a) Football
☐ b) Hockey

16. The ball may be pushed or hit with the hand, but holding the ball except in the case of a free kick is altogether disallowed.
☐ a) Football
☐ b) Hockey

17. Players must not throw any object or piece of equipment on to the field, at the ball, or at another player.
☐ a) Football
☐ b) Hockey

18. No player may be held or pulled over.
☐ a) Football
☐ b) Hockey

19. Goalkeepers or players with goalkeeping privileges must not lie on the ball.
☐ a) Football
☐ b) Hockey

20. Players must not play the ball dangerously or in a way which leads to dangerous play.
☐ a) Football
☐ b) Hockey

How Poor Were You?

Our rating of Yorkshire poverty comes courtesy of the Four Yorkshiremen sketch, written by Tim Brooke-Taylor, John Cleese, Graham Chapman and Marty Feldman and originally performed on *At Last the 1948 Show* in 1967.

Tick the box that best applies to you.

☐ a) We used to live in this tiny old tumbled-down house with great big holes in the roof.

☐ b) We used to live in one room, all twenty-six of us, no furniture, half the floor was missing, and we were all huddled together in one corner for fear of falling.

☐ c) We used to have to live in the corridor!

☐ d) We used to live in an old water tank on a rubbish tip. We got woke up every morning by having a load of rotting fish dumped all over us!

☐ e) When I say 'house', it was just a hole in the ground covered by a sheet of tarpaulin; but it was a house to us.

☐ f) We were evicted from our hole in the ground; we had to go and live in a lake.

☐ g) There were a hundred and fifty of us living in a shoebox in the middle of the road.

☐ h) We lived for three months in a rolled-up newspaper in a septic tank. We used to have to get up every morning at 6 o'clock and clean the newspaper, go to work down t' mill, fourteen hours a day, week in, week out, for sixpence a week, and when we got home our dad would thrash us to sleep with his belt.

☐ i) We used to have to get out of the lake at three o'clock in the morning, clean the lake, eat a handful of 'ot gravel, work twenty hours a day at mill for tuppence a month, come home, and Dad would beat us around the neck with a broken bottle, if we were lucky!

☐ j) We used to 'ave to get up out of shoebox in the middle of the night and lick the road clean with our tongues. We had two bits of cold gravel, worked twenty-four hours a day at mill for sixpence every four years, and when we got home our dad would slice us in two wit' breadknife.

☐ k) I had to get up in the morning at ten o'clock at night, half an hour before I went to bed, eat a lump of cold poison, work twenty-nine hours a day down mill and pay mill owner for permission to come to work, and when we got home, our Dad and our mother would kill us and dance about on our graves singing Hallelujah.

And you try telling t'young people today that. They won't believe yer!

The Answers

Round 1 – Culture & dialect

1 1st August; **2** A traditional fireside chair; **3** A ball, often made of a knot of wood, a levered wooden trap, and a bat; **4** Rushbearing; **5** A citizen of Leeds; **6** Amusement arcades; **7** Pontefract cakes; **8** Cream; **9** Kilnsey Crag; **10** Fossilised wood.

Round 2 – Entertainment

11 Mirfield; **12** Hardraw Force; **13** Hebden Bridge; **14** Giggleswick School; **15** Mount School, York; **16** Mexborough; **17** Leeds City Varieties; **18** Goathland; **19** York; **20** Tees.

Round 3 – Food & drink

21 Guiseley; **22** Wakefield, Morley and Rothwell; **23** Harrogate; **24** Henderson's Relish; **25** Wales Bar near Sheffield; **26** Copper Dragon; **27** French; **28** Oats; **29** "Let's make a proper brew"; **30** Rowntree's Chocolate Crisp.

Round 4 – Placename pictograms

31 Appletreewick; **32** Catterick; **33** Earby; **34** Featherstone.

Round 5 – In what year...

35 2005; **36** 1981; **37** 1990; **38** 1935; **39** 1978; **40** 1968; **41** 1864; **42** 1974; **43** 1972; **44** 2010.

Round 6 – Yorkshire photofit

45 Maureen Lipman (hair), Michael Parkinson (left eye), Fred Trueman (right eye), Sean Bean (nose, mouth and jaw), Richard Whiteley (clothes); **46** Geoffrey Boycott (hat, nose, mouth), Baroness Betty Boothroyd (hair), Alan Titchmarsh (eyes, clothes), Brian Blessed (beard); **47** Sir Patrick Stewart (head), Charlotte Brontë (eyes), David Hockney (glasses), William Wilberforce (nose), Harold Wilson (mouth, hand, pipe), Captain James Cook (clothes).

Round 7 – Famous firsts

48 Hansom cab; **49** NSPCC; **50** Marine Chronometer; **51** Portland cement; **52** Henry Pease; **53** Aero and KitKat; **54** Henderson's Relish; **55** Cat's eye; **56** Zebra crossings; **57** She became the first woman to conduct a Church of England wedding.

Round 8 – Literature

58 William Wordsworth; **59** Keith Waterhouse; **60** Leeds; **61** Sir John Betjeman; **62** *Wuthering Heights*; **63** York; **64** James Herriot; **65** Thirty-eight; **66** *Room at the Top*; **67** John Boynton.

Round 9 – Past times

68 Earthquake; **69** *Leeds Intelligencer*; **70** For recovering stolen property using a crystal ball; **71** Thirsk; **72** Tub boats used on the Aire and Calder Navigation; **73** Holbeck Hall; **74** Kellingley Colliery; **75** York; **76** West Riding Penny Savings Bank; **77** Scarborough.

Round 10 – People

78 Sir Titus Salt; **79** Marton; **80** Robert Thompson; **81** Ffion; **82** Jonathan Aitken; **83** Cudworth; **84** Julian Norton; **85** Prince Charles; **86** Mother Shipton; **87** Harold Wilson and Herbert Asquith.

Round 11 – Places

88 Pocklington; **89** RAF Marston Moor; **90** Halifax; **91** Mother Shipton's Cave (1630); **92** Gawthorpe; **93** The Deep, Hull; **94** Whernside, Ingleborough and Penyghent; **95** Esk; **96** On the outskirts of Boroughbridge; **97** River Wharfe.

Round 12 – Placename pictograms

98 Filey; **99** Goole; **100** Kettlewell; **101** Kippax.

Round 13 – Pot luck

102 Officially 199, though some argue there are either 200 or 198; **103** Great North Road; **104** Friday; **105** Outhwaite; **106** Asquith and Dairies; **107** St Peter; **108** Churches at Hedon and Patrington; **109** 128; **110** An ancient game once popular in Yorkshire also called Nine Men's Morris; **111** Poundworld.

Round 14 – Entertainment

112 Rotherham; **113** Leeds-born Leigh Francis (Keith Lemon); **114** Sheffield; **115** Judi Dench; **116** The Tees Transporter Bridge; **117** Annie Sugden, played by Sheila Mercier; **118** Paul Daniels; **119** Melanie Brown/Mel B; **120** Bradford; **121** *Where the Heart Is*.

Round 15 – Places

122 Lumbfoot; **123** South; **124** Skipton; **125** Bradford; **126** River Skirfare; **127** Springfield Mill in Denby Dale; **128** Nidderdale; **129** Yarm; **130** Derwent; **131** Knaresborough.

Round 16 – Bio-pics

132 Patrick Stewart; **133** David Hockney.

Round 17 – People

134 The Cottingley Fairy photographs; **135** Amanda Owen; **136** Berwick Kaler; **137** Castleford; **138** Herbert Henry Asquith; **139** Dick Turpin; **140** Eric Knight; **141** Doncaster; **142** Birstall; **143** Captain James Cook.

Round 18 – Record breakers

144 River Aire; **145** Pateley Bridge; **146** 267 miles; **147** Tan Hill Inn; **148** *Zetland* lifeboat; **149** River Bain; **150** Beverley; **151** Humber Bridge; **152** Standedge Tunnel in Huddersfield; **153** 1947.

Round 19 – Sport

154 Snooker; **155** Bradford City; **156** Michael Vaughan; **157** Leyburn; **158** Chevin Chase; **159** Kiplingcotes Derby; **160** Fattorini & Sons of Bradford; **161** Rowing (Men's coxless four and Men's eight); **162** Alan Quinn; **163** 1985; **164** Bradford City; **165** Ice hockey; **166** York racecourse; **167** Ilkley Golf Club; **168** Leeds; **169** Barnsley St Peters; **170** North Cliffe; **171** Monk Bretton; **172** Tykes; **173** Sheffield.

Round 20 – Culture & dialect

174 Lead; **175** During Lent; **176** Hogmanay; **177** Apple; **178** Whitsuntide; **179** Great (big); **180** "On Ilkla Moor Baht 'at"; **181** Without; **182** Play; **183** Hit.

Round 21 – Pot luck

184 Doncaster; **185** The Wainhouse Tower, Halifax; **186** Sir George Cayley; **187** The Middleham Jewel; **188** Skell; **189** Malham Cove; **190** Scarborough; **191** The Palace; **192** A police station; **193** It had been scalped.

Round 22 – Places

194 Sheffield; **195** Egton Bridge; **196** York; **197** Denby Dale; **198** Buckden; **199** *Erimus* (We shall be); **200** Bridlington; **201** Wharfe; **202** Swaledale and Wensleydale; **203** Catcliffe;

204 Stockeld Park; **205** Queensbury; **206** Don; **207** Boston Spa; **208** Brimham Rocks; **209** Arkengarthdale; **210** Mexborough; **211** Bingley Five Rise Locks; **212** Leeds; **213** Whitby.

Round 23 – Entertainment

214 Scholes, Holme Valley; **215** Harewood; **216** *Yanks*; **217** John Barry; **218** The Brontës; **219** Thornhill Community Academy; **220** Ripon Grammar School; **221** *In Loving Memory*; **222** Bradford Alhambra; **223** Snaiton.

Round 24 – Placename pictograms

224 Knottingley; **225** Liversedge; **226** Masham; **227** Pickering.

Round 25 – Literature

228 St Mary's Church, Beverley; **229** University of Hull; **230** *Nicholas Nickleby*; **231** Wentbridge; **232** Doncaster; **233** George Orwell; **234** Malton; **235** Tristan Farnon; **236** Charlotte Brontë; **237** Bram Stoker; **238** Alan Bennett; **239** Cædmon of Whitby; **240** *Ivanhoe*; **241** Queen's Dock, Hull; **242** Thwaite; **243** Alan Bennett and Barbara Taylor Bradford; **244** Brompton-by-Sawdon, near Scarborough; **245** Ted Hughes; **246** *The Railway Children*; **247** Emily and Anne.

Round 26 – Food & drink

248 Frumenty; **249** Cotherstone Cheese; **250** The Box Tree, Ilkley; **251** Castleford; **252** Masham; **253** Wallace and Gromit; **254** Yorkshire pudding; **255** Malton; **256** Bettys; **257** Barnsley.

Round 27 – Past times

258 Jórvík; **259** *Yorkshire Post*; **260** Leeds and Selby Railway; **261** Doncaster; **262** He was the "last of the hand-loom weavers"; **263** A gibbet or guillotine; **264** He was the first professional road builder to emerge during the Industrial Revolution; **265** Parliament; **266** Hippopotamus; **267** Flew in a balloon.

Round 28 – Pot luck

268 Halifax; **269** Surprised; **270** Bilsdale; **271** Fylingdales; **272** Horsforth; **273** Skipton; **274** Kirkstall; **275** Ripon Cathedral; **276** Wharfe; **277** St Peter's, York; **278** Dales Countryside Museum; **279** George Hotel, Huddersfield; **280** White Horse of Kilburn; **281** Cowthorpe; **282** His wife; **283** Northallerton; **284** Halifax Building Society; **285** Buttertubs Pass; **286** Conisbrough; **287** Fox's Biscuits.

Round 29 – Places

288 River Greta and River Doe; **289** Beverley; **290** Roseberry Topping; **291** Withernsea; **292** Todmorden; **293** Scarborough; **294** Wakefield; **295** Ure; **296** Nidderdale; **297** Harrogate.

Round 30 – Bio-pics

298 Sean Bean; **299** J B Priestley.

Round 31 – People

300 Brian Close; **301** Shelf; **302** Jenni Murray; **303** Sheffield; **304** Sir George Cayley; **305** Iain Macleod; **306** Helen Sharman; **307** *Mirfield Reporter*; **308** High Petergate; **309** Prince Andrew; **310** Helen Baxendale; **311** Ricky Wilson; **312** Prince Charles; **313** Thornton in Lonsdale; **314** Henry Irving; **315** Sir Fred Hoyle; **316** Lord's Cricket Ground; **317** Speaker of the House of Commons; **318** Alf Wight; **319** William Hague.

Round 32 – Entertainment

320 Arncliffe; **321** Doncaster; **322** Wakefield; **323** Kaiser Chiefs; **324** Malcolm McDowell; **325** Brighouse and Rastrick Brass Band; **326** Sheffield; **327** *Get Santa*; **328** Otley; **329** Huddersfield.

Round 33 – Famous firsts

330 Hull; **331** Stainless steel; **332** Holmfirth; **333** Joseph Priestley; **334** Joseph Bramah; **335** It is the oldest airworthy British aeroplane in the world; **336** Bailey bridge; **337** The shooting of the world's first film; **338** Beeston, Leeds; **339** The turkey.

Round 34 – Pot luck

340 It was unpaid ransom money; **341** The spring-loaded mousetrap; **342** Red Hall, Leeds; **343** Roger Iddison; **344** Bradford; **345** Kaiser Chiefs; **346** Morrisons; **347** Michael Parkinson; **348** Healaugh, near Tadcaster; **349** Mother Shipton; **350** Dorman Long of Middlesbrough; **351** Gillian Coultard; **352** Lord Mayor of Hull; **353** A narrow passageway or alley, often between terraced houses; **354** Hunslet, Leeds; **355** L S Lowry; **356** The attack on the town by the German Imperial Navy in 1914; **357** *At Last the 1948 Show*.

Round 35 – Record breakers

358 York Maze; **359** Boulby; **360** The Bingley Arms, Bardsey; **361** Otley Show; **362** Sutton-under-Whitestonecliffe; **363** Rudston, East Riding; **364** Staithes (Dog Loup); **365** Lightwater Valley; **366** Wentworth Woodhouse; **367** Otley.

Round 36 – Placename pictograms

368 Redcar; **369** Saltburn; **370** Sheffield; **371** Tadcaster.

Round 37 – Places

372 Knaresborough; **373** Barnsley; **374** Market Weighton; **375** Pickering; **376** The Forbidden Corner; **377** Goole; **378** Helmsley; **379** Hull; **380** Keld; **381** Flamingo Land; **382** Wakefield; **383** Leeds; **384** Scarborough; **385** Leyburn; **386** York; **387** Linton; **388** Derwent; **389** Beverley; **390** Londesborough; **391** Leeds and Liverpool Canal.

Round 38 – Literature

392 Sutton Bank; **393** Skipton; **394** Alderson; **395** 1847; **396** South Riding; **397** *Jane Eyre* by Charlotte Brontë; **398** Conisbrough Castle; **399** Harrogate; **400** Malham Cove; **401** *Henry VI, Part 3*; **402** *The Secret Garden* by Frances Hodgson Burnett; **403** Carperby; **404** The *Mr Men* and *Little Miss* series; **405** John Braine; **406** Top Withens; **407** Robin Hood's Bay; **408** Charlotte Brontë; **409** Ian McMillan.

Round 39 – Pot luck

410 Middlesex; **411** Gas; **412** Manningham FC; **413** Cleveland Bay; **414** Baths, sinks and toilets; **415** Marks & Spencer; **416** Airedale Terrier; **417** William Craven.

Round 40 – Bio-pics

418 Guy Fawkes; **419** Titus Salt.

Round 41 – Entertainment

420 Newby Hall, Ripon; **421** Otley; **422** John Newman; **423** Sally Wainwright; **424** Judi Dench; **425** Holme Wood, Bradford; **426** *Bradford: City of Dreams*; **427** West Yorkshire Playhouse in Leeds.

Round 42 – Record breakers

428 Ripon; **429** William Wilberforce; **430** Sheffield Football Club; **431** The Deep, Hull; **432** Rudston, East Riding; **433** Swale; **434** North York Moors; **435** Shipley Glen Tramway; **436** Flamborough Head; **437** Ebberston Hall.

Round 43 – Places

438 Barnoldswick; **439** Hull; **440** Wharfe; **441** Holmfirth; **442** Rotherham; **443** Northallerton; **444** Littondale; **445** York; **446** Robin Hood's Bay; **447** Leyburn; **448** Malham; **449** Driffield; **450** York; **451** Goldthorpe; **452** Keighley; **453** Knaresborough; **454** Northallerton; **455** Ryedale; **456** Butlin's Filey; **457** Grosmont; **458** West Witton.

Round 44 – Pot luck

459 John Gully; **460** Rotherham; **461** Samuel Smith; **462** An uncastrated male sheep/ram; **463** 21; **464** Tadcaster; **465** David Hockney; **466** Look; **467** Leeches.

Round 45 – Bio-pics

468 Ted Hughes; **469** Tony Christie.

Round 46 – Record breakers

470 Mickle Fell; **471** Ilkley; **472** Hull; **473** Tickhill; **474** Middleton Railway; **475** Drax; **476** The Cowthorpe Oak; **477** The Antient Scorton Silver Arrow.

Round 47 – Places

478 Leeds; **479** Ripon; **480** Bempton Cliffs; **481** M62 in Kirklees; **482** Horserigg Colliery, Gildersome; **483** A1; **484** Laycock, near Keighley; **485** Skidby; **486** Whitby.

Round 48 – Entertainment

487 Pontefract; **488** *The Private Life of Henry VIII*; **489** A tattoo; **490** Church Fenton; **491** Askrigg; **492** The Northern Dalesman; **493** Austerfield; **494** Joanne Froggatt; **495** Wetherby; **496** Live coverage of a Test cricket match between England and Australia at Headingley; **497** *A Boy, A Girl and a Bike*; **498** The Beautiful South; **499** "Onward Christian Soldiers"; **500** Hull; **501** The Brontë Parsonage; **502** Harry Ramsden; **503** Simon Beaufoy.

Round 49 – Yorkshire brands

504 ASDA; **505** Yorkshire Tea; **506** Cluedo; **507** First Direct; **508** ghd; **509** Seabrooks Crisps; **510** The Halifax; **511** KitKat; **512** Theakstons; **513** Marks & Spencer; **514** Morrisons; **515** Next; **516** Poundworld; **517** Silver Cross.

Round 50 – Pot luck

518 Dent; **519** Bradford; **520** Clapham; **521** Settle; **522** Richmond; **523** Wakefield and Rotherham; **524** Gormire Lake; **525** Cottingham; **526** Ilkley Moor; **527** The Georgian Theatre Royal, Richmond; **528** Holy Trinity Church, Wensley; **529** Leeds; **530** The Battle of Towton; **531** Barbara Taylor Bradford; **532** Hull; **533** *Another Man's Poison*; **534** Yorkshire Wolds; **535** Peace Babies; **536** Beggar's Bridge; **537** Burton Constable Hall; **538** Yorkshire Christmas Pie; **539** Maureen Lipman; **540** Get organised; **541** Wilfred Pickles; **542** Castle Howard; **543** Sutton Bank; **544** *The Archers*; **545** Austin Mitchell.

Round 51 – The Yorkshire Rose

546 b; **547** Score one point for *d) Nothing* if you are in the East Riding, and one point for *a) It's upside down* if you are in the North or West Ridings; **548** Score one point for *d) Nothing* if you are in the West or North Ridings, or one point for *a) It's upside down* if you are in the East Riding; **549** c (minus ten points if you selected *d) Nothing* – this is the Red Rose of Lancashire!).

Round 52 – Yorkshire filming locations

550 b (Hogsmeade Station); **551** a; **552** d; **553** c; **554** b; **555** d; **556** a; **557** b; **558** c; **559** a.

Round 53 – What city?

560 York (Micklegate, *c.*1900); **561** Bradford (Market Street, *c.*1907); **562** Leeds (Queen's Hotel and City Square, *c.*1950); **563** Hull (Paragon Street Station, *c.*early 1900s); **564** Wakefield (Westgate, date unknown); **565** Sheffield (town hall, 1938).

Round 54 – Name the view

566 From Sutton Bank/Whitestonecliffe; **567** Ribblehead Viaduct; **568** 199 Steps, Whitby; **569** Robin Hood's Bay from Ravenscar; **570** Swaledale hay meadows (Gunnerside).

Round 55 – Landmark silhouettes

571 Beverley Minster; **572** Brimham Rocks; **573** Castle Howard; **574** Bradford Alhambra; **575** Clifford's Tower; **576** Huddersfield Railway Station; **577** The Deep, Hull; **578** The Humber Bridge; **579** Penyghent; **580** Keppel's Column; **581** Leeds Corn Exchange; **582** Ribblehead Viaduct; **583** Roseberry Topping; **584** Scarborough Grand Hotel; **585** Spurn Lighthouse; **586** Salts Mill, Saltaire; **587** Bolton Priory; **588** Tees Transporter Bridge; **589** Victoria Tower on Castle Hill; **590** York Minster; **591** Cow and Calf Rocks, Ilkley Moor; **592** Whitby Abbey.

Just for fun quizzes

The Tea Test

1 a; **2** b; **3** c; **4** b; **5** c.

The Tight Test

For questions 1–21, score one point for every a, none for b. Question 22, score two points for c, one for b, none for a.

The Yorkshire Pudding Test

1 a; **2** c; **3** d; **4** c; **5** d; **6** b; **7** c; **8** b.

The Anthem Test

1 a; **2** c; **3** b; **4** c; **5** a; **6** c; **7** a; **8** c; **9** b.

The Football Test

1 a; **2** b; **3** a; **4** a; **5** a; **6** a; **7** b; **8** b; **9** a; **10** a; **11** b; **12** b; **13** b; **14** a; **15** a; **16** a; **17** b; **18** a; **19** b; **20** b.

How Poor Were You?

Only one point is on offer – no true Yorkshireman or woman would choose any answer but K!

SCALE OF
YORKSHIRENESS

Rate your Yorkshireness, from a maximum score of 650, below.

Zero: Lancastrian

1–50: Southerner

51–100: Offcumden

101–200: Fair ter middlin'

201–300: Grand

301–400: Champion

401–500: Proper Yorkshire

501–600: True Tyke

601-plus: By 'eck!

CERTIFICATE

OF YORKSHIRENESS

This is to certify that

_____

has completed t'Yorkshire Citizenship Test
wi'a score of

_____

from a maximum 650 and is now an official
citizen of God's Own Country

Picture credits

Yorkshire rose (cover): public domain; piggy bank (cover) © BSGStudio; teapot (cover): public domain; Yorkshire rose (p4, p69, p84): CC BY-SA 3.0; cat (p9) © BSGStudio; hay bale (p9) © CharlesLeon; file (p17) © freevector; dog (p21) © hannamonika; rabbit in hat (p21): public domain; beef stew (p21) © jeffreyw: CC BY 2.0; heart (p21): public domain; diary page (p21): unknown; VHS (p21) © Toby Hudson: CC BY-SA 2.5 AU; wine (p21) © Regi51: CC BY-SA 2.5; statue (p21) © Jörg Bittner Unna: CC BY 3.0; sheep-shearing (p39) © -JvL-: CC BY 2.0; coffee bean (p39) © Chiccodoro: CC BY-SA 2.0; jay (p39) © Luc Viatour / www.Lucnix.be: CC BY-SA 3.0; bumblebee (p39) © Alvesgaspar: CC BY-SA 3.0; vicar (p39) © Gareth Hughes: CC BY 2.5; Lee Evans (p39) © Phil Guest: CC BY-SA 2.0; car (p47) © veernavya; penny for the guy (p53) © Paddy Patterson: CC-BY-2.0; forks (p53) © Jonatan Svensson Glad: CC-BY-SA 4.0; spanner (p53) © Saulius Vaivada; donkey (p53) © MARIE JEANNE Iliescu; salt cellar (p53) © aschaeffer; teddy bear (p59) © Jean Scheijen; sheep (p59) © proman77; foot (p59) © Nihan Aydin; statue (p59) © Jörg Bittner Unna: CC BY 3.0; Sermon on the Mount, by Carl Bloch (p59): public domain; teabag (p59) © Konrad Socha; Lancashire rose (p69): CC BY-SA 3.0; Goathland Station (p70): public domain; Hardraw Force (p70) © Wehha: CC BY-SA 3.0; Kilnsey Crag (p70) © ianpudsey: CC BY 3.0; Holmfirth (p70) © Harry Wood: CC BY-SA 2.5; Oakworth Station (p71) © RuthAS: CC BY 4.0; Askrigg (p71) © Kreuzschnabel: CC BY-SA 3.0; Castle Howard (p71): public domain; Harewood House (p71) © Gunnar Larsson: CC BY-SA 3.0; Carl Wark (p71) © 2009, Jeremy Atherton: CC BY-SA 3.0; Tees Transporter Bridge (p71) © Jon Oakley: CC BY 2.0; old post-cards (p72): copyright unknown; Sutton Bank (p73) © Welcome to Yorkshire; Ribblehead Viaduct (p73) © Michael Bryan: CC BY 2.0; 199 Steps, Whitby (p73) © RevDave: CC BY-SA 3.0; Robin Hood's Bay from Ravenscar (p73) © Reiner Tegtmeyer: CC BY-SA 2.0; Gunnerside meadows (p73) © Kreuzschna-bel: CC BY-SA 3.0; ornament (p78) © advayta; teapot (p78) © Amili; ornament (p79) © advayta; wallet (p79) © owattaphotos; ornament (p81) © advayta; Yorkshire puddings (p82) © FomaA; ornament (p83) © advayta; football (p84) © www.webdesignhot.com; ornament (p86) © advayta; border (p95) © digiselector.

All logos on pages 64–65 belong to the copyright holders